This book has been based on the true happenings at 'Bide a Wee' my home for over twenty years. It had a beautiful garden which brought me a lot of happiness, plus a lot of hard work! The wild life etc became the characters for my book, it's been a joy getting it all together!

I thank those who supported and inspired me to write the rhyming stories.

Author

Hazel M Foster

Animal and Garden Adventures

Hunsy, Thumps and Friends!

Volume 1

Author

Hazel M Foster

Illustrator

Dawn S Taylor

hmwfoster@talktalk.net

ISBN: 978-0-9957755-0-3

Thumps

'Bide a Wee'

Would you like to meet new friends?
They're such good company!
Hunsy and Thumps - welcome you
To their home at 'Bide a Wee'

.

Lady

Hunsy

Contents

Hunsy's Home

Hunsy's really full of fun, when she goes out to play
Her home is always nice and clean, she sweeps it every day
Her friend Thumps, if he calls in, she greets him with a smile
She likes to give him food to eat, if he can stay awhile.

They often visit bluebell wood, to hear the sweet birds sing
Thumps has a lot of jobs to do, as he takes care of everything!
The grass is soft beneath their feet, when it's warm and sunny
Away from noise, and traffic fumes, it's perfect for a bunny.

Hunsy has so many friends, they always help her out!
She knows that she can call on them, whenever they're about
They all have different jobs to do, everything's well planned
The garden keeps them busy, as they have a lot of land.

Hunsy has a special friend, her fur is soft and black
She can climb the tallest trees, she's not a rabbit but a cat
Hunsy is very contented, with her friends at 'Bide a Wee'
There's always someone there, to keep her company.

Lady the Cat

Hunsy treasures Lady, she is her closest friend
They love it in the garden, so many things they tend
Lady sometimes climbs the trees, she never seems to fear
Hunsy doesn't worry too much, as long as she is near.

Lady likes to come and go, she has her own cat flap
She waits for Hunsy to brush her, after she's had a nap
When it comes to meal times, she's there right on the dot
She really loves her biscuits, her feeder has got a clock.

When she knows it's bedtime, she gets on Hunsy's bed
She doesn't go out late at night, she snuggles up instead
Danger is always out there, it's not safe for pussy cats
As other creatures roam the night, maybe even rats!

Lady gets up bright and early, while Hunsy's still asleep
She never ever makes a noise, as she knows how to creep
Lady's there to guard the home, she keeps the mice at bay
They don't want uninvited guests, in case they try to stay!

Beaky the Pigeon

Hunsy looked out her window, the pigeons were everywhere!
Beaky came with all his pals, he'd said "There was food to spare"
They trampled all over the garden, looking for something to eat
Beaky sat on the bird feeder, when he heard a little bird tweet.

"Go away you naughty pigeons", said a blue tit flying around
"That's our bird seed, Hunsy's put there, yours is on the ground"
Beaky nearly lost his balance, "There's plenty of seed here for us
You must learn to share your food, and not make such a fuss".

The little bird hopped around, "I'm going to tell Ollie the Owl
When he hears you're pinching our food, it will make him scowl"
Beaky laughed, "You can't scare me he keeps us awake all night
He sits there hooting for hours on end, he is an awesome sight".

Hunsy felt she'd heard enough, "Look here my feathered friends
There is plenty of food for everyone, before this winter ends!
The shrubs and trees will blossom soon with berries you can eat
God he provided for all of us - each one has a special treat".

Vinnnie the Van

Vinnie lives at home with Thumps, he's not too far away
They love him here at 'Bide a Wee' they all want him to stay
He is white with sliding doors, the tools are kept safe inside
Hunsy gets really excited, when he takes them for a ride.

Vinnnie's eyes open up wide, when he's on country lanes
Potholes are a real problem, sometimes he really complains
"The Councils are responsible, they should fill them all in!
If someone had an accident, they'd make an awful din".

He's always very careful, when he's on the motorway
Most cars like to overtake, he feels they make him sway!
If Vinnie's helping Hunsy, he doesn't like hanging about
"I'm all ready to get going", the others hear him shout.

Thumps is very fond of Vinnie, he never lets him down
With plenty of room in the back, he's ready to go to town
He goes on journeys everywhere, he has travelled miles!
He's very happy on the road - at cars he always smiles.

Tommy the field Mouse

Hunsy had an awful shock, as she lay there half asleep!
She heard a noise, a rustling sound, it came from her en'suite
She sat up very quickly, then she leaped up from her bed!
Tommy sat there washing his face, "Morning Huns" he said.

"What are you doing?" said Hunsy, "You have got a cheek
This bedroom it belongs to me, especially my en'suite!"
Tommy washed behind his ears, and gave a great big yawn
"I really had a lovely sleep, I was up at the crack of dawn".

"How did you get in?" said Hunsy, "Did you climb up the wall?
Then get in through my window, you're lucky you didn't fall?
You can't stay here, it's not right, I'm going to catch you now"
She grabbed him by his tail, then she trapped him in her towel.

"I don't know how you got in here but you belong outside"
Hunsy held on tight to him "Please let me go" Tommy cried
"Lady the cat she brought me in, she held me in her jaws!
She was very kind to me, she said - "My home is yours".

Willy the Worm

Hunsy has another friend, his name is, Willy the worm
He always works so very hard, when there is earth to turn!
Wriggling here and wriggling there, he has such a lot to do
He digs the earth every day to help the seeds grow through.

He's such a funny creature, he looks the same both ends
He hasn't any eyes to see, as he twists around the bends
Danger is never far away, whenever he comes up for air!
Birds are always on the lookout, for a tasty worm to share.

He's also prone to accidents, if Hunsy is digging around
He keeps on ducking and diving, deep beneath the ground
A friend of his got chopped in half, although he didn't die!
Two halves went their separate ways as they waved goodbye.

Willy plus friends and family, love living at 'Bide a Wee'
There's always lots of work to do they all like helping Hunsy
A worm is a very special friend, so treat him with respect!
The garden is his haven - especially when it's wet.

Winnie the Wasp

Winnie was chasing Hunsy, "I want to play" she said
"Go away" she cried out, "Stop buzzing round my head
I got badly stung last year, and my foot was full of pain!
I really feared that it was you, as you all look the same".

"It wasn't me" said Winnie, "I wouldn't do that to you!
I use my sting to defend myself, you people scare me too"
"Okay" said Hunsy "Follow me I need to pick some plums"
Winnie was delighted, "I'd like you to meet my chums".

Hunsy really had a shock, the wasps were everywhere
They were eating all her plums, they didn't want to share
She tried to pick one off the tree but saw a wasp inside!
"Please don't sting me eat the rest" Hunsy quickly cried.

She picked up her empty bucket, "Goodbye everyone
It's been really nice meeting you all, I've had a lot of fun"
Winnie was quickly by her side, "Let me see you home"
"Stay where you are" said Hunsy "I'm okay on my own!".

13

Freddie the Frog

Freddie is the cutest frog, he leaps and bounds around!
He lives in the pond with all the fish, sunken in the ground
You'll see him swimming happily, with friends and family
The fish they make him welcome, here at 'Bide a Wee'.

He's a cheeky little chap, with eyes on the top of his head
He watches everything you do, he's fat and looks well fed!
Freddie's life began as a tadpole, he swam around very fast
He was brave and determined, that he was going to last.

When his arms and legs grew, he leaped out of the pond
Freddie was very curious, as he wondered what lay beyond!
He landed safely on some stones, then he hid beneath a plant
He felt a little frightened but there's no such word as can't.

He sat there thinking this is fun but then he got a fright!
Lady the cat was out for a stroll, she was an awesome sight
She placed her paw on Freddie, he almost died of fear!
Hunsy came to the rescue - then watched him disappear.

Bertie the Bumble Bee

Bertie's a very busy bee, he pollinates the flowers
He settles on the blossom, buzzing around for hours!
Sometimes you'll see him resting, nestling in the grass
He's furry and quite fearless, be careful when you pass.

Hunsy's not too sure of him, she really fears his sting
She's always very wary, when she says, - Hello to him
One day around the bonfire, he caught her in his sight!
He followed her down the garden, she had an awful fright.

"I didn't mean to disturb you" she apologized to him
"I'm only playing Hunsy" he said, he had a cheeky grin
"I've got lots of work to do, as I'm busy making honey
When it's sold in fancy jars, it makes a lot of money".

Lady the cat then paid her respects, "Hello Mr Bee
I'll never try to catch you again, it was very foolish of me"
"Don't worry my dear" said Bertie "You were very young
You didn't mean to hurt me - you were only having fun".

Ted the Tractor

Ted was busy cutting the grass, when he noticed all the moss!
"That looks unsightly" he said to Hunsy, "It makes me really cross
It's a job for Scotty the scarifier, he told me he's still unemployed
He wants to work, he's not lazy but some things he likes to avoid".

Thumps put the weed and feed down, "The moss is almost dead!
Grass always looks much greener, when it's watered and well fed
Scotty can rake up all the dead moss, it shouldn't take him long
He has the teeth to tackle the job, they're long and very strong".

Ted finished cutting all the grass, Hunsy brushed him down
"You really have worked hard today, you really went to town"
He was feeling rather tired but still moaning about the moss!
"Get in touch with Scotty today, he's fallen out with his boss".

"Okay" said Hunsy "Don't worry, I'll have a word with Thumps
Scotty can get a lift in his van, he could come over here at once!
I'm sure he'll be happy working again, seeing all his old chums
We'll tidy up the garden now - before the winter comes".

Scotty the Scarifier

Scotty looked at Hunsy"s grass, "It looks a mess" he said
"It's full of weeds and dead moss, if left it's going to spread!
I'm free next week to do the job, I'll rake out all the rubbish
Thumps can take it to the tip, then the grass will flourish".

Hunsy was delighted, she wanted her grass to look good
She was proud of everything, she loved her neighbourhood!
"I'll patch it up with grass seed, it's had some weed and feed
I'm going to have a perfect lawn without a single weed".

Scotty started work early, his teeth tearing into the ground!
The moss and the weeds lay on the top, spread into a mound
Monty the motor mower said, "I'll gather up all the rubbish"
It really didn't take them long, Hunsy watched them finish.

Hunsy said, "You've done a good job" she was very pleased
She mixed the seed with compost, when suddenly she sneezed
Her nose it started twitching, "I'm allergic to pollen and grass
I'll have to go indoors" she said "Next time I'll wear a mask".

Eric the Earwig

Eric was looking for a home, he had a large family!
He found a bag of garden waste, "This will do for me"
Hunsy was busy gardening, "Hello there Eric" she said
"I'm cutting back the flowers, some of them are dead".

She filled the empty bags up, then she tidied all around
The sun was shining brightly, she also hoed the ground!
Henry the hedgehog was fast asleep, inside his little home
He only ventures out at night, when he wants to roam.

She placed the bags against a wall, Eric crawled inside
"This will make a perfect home, somewhere we can hide"
He moved in very quickly, he didn't want Hunsy to see!
"There's room enough for everyone, for all my family".

Thumps arrived in his van, "I'll take those bags to the tip"
He placed them carefully in the back, Eric felt quite sick
His family crawled all over the place, trying to escape!
"Help us" Eric cried out loud, "Before it is too late".

Robbie the Robin

Robbie is such a friendly bird, he hops about all day!
Hunsy loves to watch him, when he comes out to play
Known as robin the red breast, he stands out in a crowd
Such a cheeky little chap, his chirping sounds quite loud.

When Hunsy starts to dig around, he keeps her company
He chirps away and hops about, then flies from tree to tree
He loves a tasty worm to eat, he hopes she'll find him one
Willy the worm is underground, for him it's not much fun!

Robbie has a lot of friends, he likes the cockney sparrow
He loves to sneak a ride - on top of Wally the wheelbarrow
The gardens always full of birds, the pigeons love the bath
Hunsy sits and watches them, they always make her laugh.

Robbie is very cautious, when Lady the cat is about
He always keeps his distance, as it doesn't pay to flout!
She might pounce and grab him, if mistaken for a mouse
He knows he is much safer - when she is in the house.

Henry the Hedgehog

The problem with Henry, he's so prickly to hold
If ever he feels threatened, his prickles they unfold!
He knows that they protect him, so he rolls into a ball
He really is quite clever, although he's only small.

He loves the summer evenings, if he goes for a stroll
Searching for a tasty meal, he hopes he'll find in a bowl!
The roads are a very dangerous place, for this little chap
He mustn't stop or linger, it's not safe to have a nap.

Henry needs to hibernate, when winter comes around
He looks for somewhere cozy, he sleeps without a sound
He noticed Hunsy's bonfire, it looked so safe and warm!
He made a bed and snuggled up, then he began to yawn.

Others came and joined him, his Aunts and cousins too
They cuddled close together, to sleep the winter through
A bonfire, is a very dangerous place, for anyone to be!
There are much safer places - here at 'Bide a Wee'.

Jimmy the Jet Wash

Jimmy stood to attention, "This is just the job for me!
I was trained in the navy, I washed all the ship decks at sea"
Hunsy beamed a great big smile, as she was very impressed
"The patios very dirty" she said, "You must do your best".

Jimmy really loves his job, he enjoys washing things down
Spud the spider was most upset, "Me and the kids will drown
You should be more careful, my homes been washed away
Now we have nowhere to live, someone has got to pay".

"I'm very sorry" said Jimmy, "But Hunsy will help you out
Her shed is warm and cozy, with more room to move about"
Spud was very grateful, his family they quickly moved in!
Hilda his wife loved the shed, she had a new web to spin.

Jimmy continued working, until everything looked clean
He felt really sorry for Spud, as it's not like him to be mean
"All's well, that ends well", said Hunsy, with her big smile!
'Bide a Wee' looked beautiful - Scottish for stay awhile.

Stan the Strimmer

Stan is very proud of his job, he keeps the borders neat
He is very careful, when he's striming near Hunsy's feet!
He never likes to hang about, so it doesn't take him long
His plastic line to strim the grass, is fine but very strong.

He's very happy with his mates, they all live in the shed
They go on talking for hours on end, before they go to bed
Monty the motor mower, is very good at cutting the grass!
Stan quickly follows him around, they both move very fast.

Hunsy was very pleased with them, "You two need to rest
The grass looks really beautiful, you always do your best!
You need to go back in the shed, they say it's going to rain
There's another day tomorrow, it soon comes round again".

Hunsy loves her garden, she works outside for hours!
Everyone has different jobs, she likes to tend the flowers
They all get on well together, each must pull their weight
Teamwork is the answer - to get things nice and straight.

Cecil the Seagull

Hunsy felt very upset, "The seagulls scare me" she said!
"When they swoop down I'm wary, I always duck my head
The other birds don't like them, everyone's staying away
It isn't fair on all of us, the garden is somewhere to play".

Hunsy bought some chicken thighs to make a casserole!
She tossed the skin onto the grass, and then she saw a seagull
Suddenly the sky was full, of seagulls squawking out loud!
Cecil flew down and grabbed the skin, he was very proud.

Off he went, flapping his wings, as he soared into the sky!
Hunsy couldn't believe her eyes, she wished that she could fly
The greedy seagulls ate the lot, swooping down to the ground
Beaky the pigeon he looked on but he didn't make a sound!

Hunsy was really angry, "They're a thieving lot" she said
"I'm going to report this to Ollie the Owl before I go to bed
He'll call another meeting, we'll all have a lengthy debate!
Cecil's always taking liberties – this is a private estate".

Fred the Shed

Fred was feeling really sad, "I'm looking so old!" he said
"I'm covered in dirt and green mould, who wants a dirty shed?"
He really feared for the future, he'd been sheltering everyone
The working tools, they rest in him, when their work is done.

Hunsy said, "I'll wash you down, and then I'll paint you again
I wouldn't leave you to suffer, you keep us all dry from the rain"
Monty the motor mower said, "You are still a very strong shed
I always feel safe and happy, tucked up in my cozy warm bed".

Jimmy the jet wash set to work, the mould soon disappeared!
Fred he shivered, "Wow that felt cold!" everyone they cheered
"It's pouring with rain, I'm soaking wet" Ted the tractor said
"We'll have a lazy time today, we'll be able to stay in bed".

Fred was feeling much better, the sun made him feel warm
Hunsy gave him a new coat of paint, he felt he'd been reborn!
She cleaned and polished his window, so he was able to see
All his friends around him - who lived at 'Bide a Wee'.

Maggie the Magpie

Maggie is a crafty bird, her feathers are black and white
She comes across as aggressive, always spoiling for a fight!
She struts around the garden, as though she owns the place!
Beaky the pigeon ignores her, he prefers the human race.

Hunsy gets quite cross with her, she makes an awful noise
She sits there squawking in the trees, as attention she enjoys
Maggie is always on the lookout, she never misses a trick!
When she visits with her mates, things get rather hectic!

She really is a show off, they say she comes from France
Hunsy likes to watch her, when she does her funny dance!
Her legs are black and shiny, it's like she's got stockings on
The other birds don't like her, they're glad to see her gone.

"We don't want her" said Beaky, "She always causes trouble
I wouldn't want her as my mate, not someone I could cuddle"
Hunsy said, "Now listen to me, we don't need more enemies!
You should try to welcome her – it's always best to please".

Sid the Snake

Freddie the frog was screaming, "Someone help me please"
Sid had Freddie inside his mouth, his jaws began to squeeze!
Hunsy was busy cleaning the pond, when she saw Sid the snake
At first she thought, he was dead, she'd made a big mistake!

Hunsy hooked Sid from the pond, he tried to slither away
She pressed the hook into his neck, she couldn't let him stray
Freddie's head and arms hung out, he'd almost disappeared!
"Please let me go" cried Freddie - death is what he feared.

Hunsy was very determined, "Let go of Freddie" she said
She put more pressure on the hook, "Let go or you'll be dead"
Sid he found, he couldn't breathe, he gave a great big gasp!
Freddie managed to free himself, he had to move real fast.

He quickly leaped into the pond, then swam away and hid!
Donnie the fish said, "What's up mate be careful of that Sid?"
Hunsy let Sid slither away, she was hoping he'd go next door
But he lay on the compost heap - annoyed he didn't score!

Scary the Scarecrow

Scary is always welcome when he visits, 'Bide a Wee'
He sometimes feels cold and hungry, in need of company
It must get very lonely, when he's out there on his own!
His job is so important, when seeds have just been sown.

Scary lives across the way, he works for farmer John
He has to scare the birds away, he flaps until they've gone
He knows he mustn't fall asleep, or he will lose his job!
The birds they never hesitate, to scavenge and to rob.

When it's wet and windy, Scary always feels the cold
He's hoping to find another job, before he gets too old!
One day he called at Hunsy's door, looking for some work
He also had good references, and said he'd never shirk.

Hunsy said she'd let him know, there's always jobs to do!
Her chimney lets in dampness, as the rain is getting through
Lady the cat walked past him, she purred and said, "Hello"
Scary said "Thanks for the tea it's late now, I must go".

Ollie the Owl

Ollie is a special bird, he's so wise and very cool
It doesn't do to cross him, or to take him for a fool!
His education was top of the list - at the university!
He passed with flying colours, to live at 'Bide a Wee'.

Environmental problems, he's happy to sort out!
His education always helps, if ever he should doubt
Law is law to be obeyed, he likes to keep things calm
His feathers never ruffled, he has a certain charm.

Hunsy feels so very proud, he chose to stay with her
It's strange that he has feathers, why doesn't he have fur?
He never goes to sleep at night, he watches everything
At night you hear him hooting, he doesn't really sing.

Ollie has eyes like Lady the cat, both can see in the dark
He likes to hunt throughout the night, as happy as a lark!
Hunsy and Lady sleep soundly, she's such a sleepy head
When it comes to night time - you're better off in bed.

Hilda and Spud the Spiders

Hilda sat up in the corner, her web was fine but strong
Spud he keeps his distance, in case something goes wrong!
Hilda was looking very depressed, she hadn't eaten all day
"I'm feeling rather hungry but nothing comes my way".

Hilda was getting broody, Spud shivered at the thought!
"I can't afford to cuddle her, as its curtains if you're caught"
He edged his way around the web, he wanted to talk to Hunsy
He toppled over, fell to the ground, Hilda shouted "Clumsy!".

Hunsy was busy pruning the trees, she was heading their way
Spud climbed quickly onto the web, he was trying to get away
Hunsy started cutting a branch, when the web began to move!
Hilda shouted "What's going on" she really didn't approve.

Hunsy continued to prune the tree, she noticed Hilda's web
It shimmered in the sunlight, "It's really beautiful" she said
"Hello Spud the spider, I didn't mean to disturb your home
I'm sorry if I frightened you - this tree has really grown".

Harry the Hedge Cutter

Harry sat clenching his teeth, "Where is Thumps?" he said
"I'm all ready to cut the hedge, I could have stayed in bed"
Thumps he opened up the shed, "Good morning everyone!
Come on Harry, it's time for work, its lovely in the sun".

Hunsy plugged his lead in, "This shouldn't take us long"
Harry started grinding his teeth, they were very strong!
The hedge was rather prickly, with brambles sticking out
Harry cut right through them, he didn't hang about!

When the hedge was finished, he went back in the shed
"I'm feeling very tired" he said, and laid back on his bed!
Stan the strimmer smiled at him, "You did well my friend"
That work it can be dangerous, it never seems to end".

Hunsy cleared up all the mess, everything looked neat!
"It's raining" said Ronald the rake, "You will get wet feet"
She quickly locked the sheds up, "Good night everyone
What a lovely day it's been - we've had a lot of fun".

Ratty the Rat

People don't like Ratty, he's not welcome in the house
If you really had to choose, most would prefer a mouse!
Rats have a bad reputation, they're always in the wrong
If Ratty lived in London, he wouldn't survive very long.

Some rats live in the sewers, they never see the sun!
It's not their fault they're born there, it's not a lot of fun
They go into people's houses, searching for their food!
They need to eat to survive, rats are also very shrewd.

Ratty lives in the country, where all the fields are green
He's large and rather handsome, he's never really mean!
Hunsy saw him moving about, next door to 'Bide aWee'
He popped out, then said "Hello" he wanted company.

Rats can be very gentle, some people keep them as pets
If they're feeling poorly, you can take them to the vets!
They're very soft and cuddly but Hunsy can't have one
Lady the cat would be very upset, as she is number one!

Camilla the Cow

Hunsy was getting worried, Camilla the cow next door
Wanted to graze on Hunsy's land, and she was out to score!
"I respect her as my neighbour, as she used to be my friend
But now she's mooing all day long, my land I must defend".

Camellia was very bossy, "It's my hedge" she mooed out loud
"I'm going to make you move over, and I shall win" she vowed
Hunsy was very determined, "Although she's bigger than me!
I will fight to the bitter end, for my land here at 'Bide a Wee'''.

Hunsy consulted Ollie the owl, "She mustn't get her own way
The witch who lives in the magic tree, will blow her plans away
She'll dance around her bonfire, then she'll cast a magic spell!
Camilla's plans will come to an end but no one here must tell".

"She needs to learn a lesson, she can't have all her own way
It would be best if she moved on, as no one wants her to stay"
Hunsy breathed a sigh of relief, "I'm going to live here forever!
Thumps will always help me out - we work so well together".

The Magic Tree

Hunsy's proud of her magic tree, the tallest she's ever seen!
Its sixty foot high, and forty feet wide, a beautiful evergreen
Home to many of her friends, it protects them night and day
When it's rough and windy, the branches always sway!

Pip the squirrel is an acrobat, he's always taking chances!
He swings around so dangerously, clinging onto the branches
The birds they chase each other around, as in and out they fly
Hunsy, she loves the pigeons, they build their nests up high.

When Lady the cat was a kitten, she climbed the magic tree
Then she disappeared from sight, it really frightened Hunsy!
"Come on down you naughty girl" she waited there in vain!
She couldn't see her little friend but she came down again.

"Where did you go?" said Hunsy "You mustn't climb so high
I thought you had gone forever, as I could barely see the sky!
It looked so bleak and dark up there, I really feared for you"
"Don't be silly" said Lady, "It's something us cats like to do".

Batty the Bat

Batty is rather scary, she always flies around so fast!
Unlike a bird she's a mammal, and her reputations vast
She's very small and furry, in flight her wings expand!
Covered finely with a skin, they help her to fly and land.

Hunsy's not too sure of her but she always says, "Hello"
Batty never stops in flight, she keeps whizzing to and fro!
When dawn breaks, she flies home, then falls fast asleep
You'll find her hanging upside down, if you care to peep.

Bats are known as vampires, who many people fear!
Batty's really rather sweet but she doesn't want you near
She's also blind and cannot see, she navigates with radar!
Its warnings guide her all the time, whether near or far.

She's found the perfect place to live, here at 'Bide a Wee'
When dusk arrives you'll see her, diving from tree to tree
No one really bothers her, she knows she's safe in flight!
Lady the cat prefers to sleep - on Hunsy's bed at night.

Woody the Woodpecker

Woody is a colourful bird but he's an uninvited guest!
Hunsy's not too pleased with him, she thinks he is a pest
He likes drilling holes in trees, his beak is very strong!
He never seems to tire or rest, he's at it all day long.

Hunsy has a large willow tree, its sixty feet in height
It's always looked so beautiful but now it looks a sight!
Woody's been busy every day, drilling a great big hole
Now with branches weakened, the wind soon took its toll.

The tree began to split in half but it didn't worry Woody
He returned and drilled again, Hunsy said "How could he?"
Then one day disaster struck, as half the tree came down!
"Woody is to blame for this" said Hunsy with a frown.

It really was a problem, she just didn't know what to do!
Thumps said, "It needs clearing it's going to spoil the view"
She found a man to fell the tree, who wanted logs to burn
Woody kept at a safe distance - but will he ever learn?

Donnie the Fish

Donnie lives in Hunsy's pond, along with all his mates
A large white fish, he eats a lot, the heron he really hates!
It's always on the lookout, a bird so fearsome and strong
It has a beak that's razor sharp, its legs are very long.

A heron doesn't hesitate, when hungry in need of food!
Hector swoops down uninvited, his manners rather crude
He gobbles up the fish so fast, they never stand a chance
They always need protecting, from a herons evil glance.

Donnie loves ducking and diving, he acts like a whale!
Hunsy sits and watches him, he dives then flips his tail
The other fish follow him, swimming around the pond
They've all grown up together, so now there is a bond.

Freddie the frog lives in the pond, in perfect harmony
The pond is a very peaceful place, here at 'Bide a Wee'
Hunsy likes feeding the fish, Lady the cat sits with her!
If you listen very carefully - you'll hear her gently purr.

Hector the Heron

Hector isn't welcome when he comes to, 'Bide a Wee'
All the fish are filled with fear, he even frightens Donnie!
When the dawn breaks, he flies down, most are still asleep
His greedy eyes can see the fish, he's ready with his beak.

He likes to step into the pond, his legs are thin and long
The fish are in great danger, Hector's large and very strong!
He scoops them up and flies away, he then returns for more
He feasts until there's no fish left, he's really out to score.

Hunsy always fears for the fish, they need to be protected
Hector won't try, stepping into the pond, if it's safely netted
Another way that stops him, is to place some string around!
He can't risk, being caught up, then stumbling on the ground.

It's peaceful in the summer time, when Hector's out at sea
The fish can relax and sunbathe, when it's warm and sunny
The pond is a very safe place, as there's no one else to fear
But Hector will return again - as winter time draws near.

Goldie the Goldfish

Goldie lay there dying, she had fallen from the sky!
Fish they don't have any wings, they're not meant to fly
Hector the heron had stolen her, from a neighbour's pond
He had his evil eyes on her, someone else he's wronged.

Goldie was in an awful state, "Help me someone please
Night-times coming very soon, and I don't want to freeze"
She needed to be in clean water, before it became too late
Goldie lay there praying, was this going to be her fate?

Hunsy was in the garden, she looked down to the ground
Goldie lay there covered in dirt, "Look what I have found"
Hunsy bathed her in clean water, she was barely still alive
Goldie was grateful, to be saved, so desperate to survive.

She was kept in intensive care, with special medication
She fought hard, to stay alive, she caused a big sensation!
Lady the cat peered into the tank, "Hello there" she purred
Goldie could barely see her, as everything looked blurred.

Goldie meets Donnie

Goldie was very excited, she'd waited for this special day
She was going to meet Donnie the fish, he wanted her to stay
At last she had recovered, after long months, in the aquarium!
Memories still haunted her, when stolen by Hector the heron.

When Hector flew over the magic tree, with Goldie in his beak
Pip the squirrel sat up and shouted, "Hey let go of her you freak"
Hector lost his balance with shock, when he shouted back at him
He dropped Goldie from his beak, her chances were very slim.

The magic tree it saved her fall, as she tumbled to the ground
With no one there to comfort her, she prayed she would be found
Hunsy came to the rescue, her prayers had been answered at last
She helped her to get better saying, "You must forget the past".

Donnie was up bright and early, things were getting warmer
He longed to meet Goldie the fish, he'd heard about her trauma!
Hunsy lowered her into the pond, beneath the bright blue sky
Donnie said "Welcome home, you were never meant to die".

Pip the Squirrel

Pip loves chasing everywhere, he never stops to rest!
He darts about all over the place, he's always full of zest
He's cheeky, and sometimes naughty, a very busy chap
You never see him resting, like his friend the pussycat.

His tail is long and bushy, with fur that's very thick
It helps him leap, from tree to tree, he must be really fit!
He gathers nuts for wintertime, then when he hibernates
He always has some tasty food, for him and all his mates.

The winter time is very cold but Pip he doesn't moan
He keeps warm and cozy, there's no place like his home
He moves around very fast but when he's standing still
He looks just like a statue, and you wonder if he's real.

Lady tries to chase him but he's much too fast for her!
A cat could never catch him, a mouse she'd much prefer
A squirrel is never dangerous, its fun to watch him play
Although he is a rodent – we all want him to stay.

Kev the Cockerel

Hunsy had fallen fast asleep but she was in for a big surprise
Kev was outside crowing out loud, she couldn't believe her eyes
He'd come right into her garden, along with the rest of his brood!
Scraping and digging the flowers up, searching for chicken food.

Lady and Hunsy were disgusted, "How dare he invite himself!
Does he know what he's eating, it might not be good for his health"
Hunsy thought, this has got to stop, Thumps would know what to do
"Don't worry" he said, "I have a plan to stop them coming through".

He erected wire fencing along, he didn't want Hunsy to worry!
They stopped to eat their carrots but they knew they had to hurry
Kev was crowing across the way, he had planned on a visit again
When he saw the chicken wire, he was foiled by his own game.

Hunsy and Lady slept soundly that night, everyone was happy
Kev didn't try to intrude again, he's not welcome at 'Bide a Wee'
He had to be taught a lesson, he couldn't have all his own way
Some rules and regulations - are meant for us all to obey!

Hunsy goes to Hollywood

Hunsy was getting excited, "I'm going to Hollywood"
Pip the squirrel laughed, "In your dreams maybe you could"
"I've written a special book" she said, "It's my autobiography
It's about my life and all my friends, here at 'Bide a Wee'".

Ollie the owl he hooted, "You could be wasting your time!
You need to be more educated, it's easy making words rhyme
I studied at the university, and I passed all their lengthy exams
I'm qualified now for anything but I don't have any real plans".

Hunsy became despondent, she wondered if he was right!
"I've always had stars in my eyes, I'd love to see Snow White
I also want to meet Mickey Mouse, they all live in Disneyland
I won't be gone forever, I thought you would all understand".

Lady the cat reassured her, "None of us wants you to leave
Maybe you will become famous but it's rather hard to believe!
We need you here at 'Bide a Wee' it wouldn't seem the same"
Hunsy unpacked her suitcase - friends come first not fame!

Hunsy has some other friends
You'll meet them in volume two!
They've waited very patiently
With lots more fun for you.

Rhyming Stories by Hazel M Foster

Illustrated by Dawn S Taylor

Animal and Garden Adventures

Hunsy, Thumps and Friends!

Volume 1

Author

Hazel M Foster

I dedicate this book to my friend Gerda

Made in the USA
Columbia, SC
02 September 2018